MAXIMUM RIDE

W9-APU-363

Instilled with avian DNA in a lab known as the "School," Max and her family escaped confinement with the help of scientist Jeb Batchelder, who they believed perished assisting them. When the youngest of the flock, Angel, is abducted by the lab's foot soldiers – shape-shifting men and women infused with lupine DNA called Erasers – led by Jeb's son, Ari, Max discovers that Jeb is not only alive, but still working with the School! Rescuing Angel, the flock heads to New York City to find the "Institute," which they believe holds the secrets to their past. While raiding the facility, though, they are again confronted by Jeb and his Erasers. The flock manages to get away, but not before Max accidentally kills Ari!

Now the flock is off to Washington, D.C., following up a lead on their parents, but Max can't escape the mysterious voice that's begun whispering inside her head – or Jeb's haunting words that in killing Ari, she may have killed her own brother...

MAXIMUM
RIDE

MAXIMUM
RIDE
CHAPTER 16

YOU KILLED YOUR OWN BROTHER!

PLASH!

!!

THAT CAN'T BE TRUE!

FLINCH!

YOU OKAY?

You look pale.

HOW DO YOU MEAN?

MAX, WHAT'S THAT?

CHOP-PERS?

TOO SMALL AND QUIET FOR THAT. BIRDS, MAYBE?

!!

WAIT, THOSE...

...THOSE AREN'T BIRDS.

...IT CAN'T BE...

LET'S SPLIT UP.

NUDGE! GAZZY! NINE O'CLOCK! ANGEL, UP TOP, MOVE IT!

IGGY AND FANG, FLANK ME FROM BELOW!

SWISH!

YIKES! GET AWAY!

S.P.I.N

THEY'RE TOO BIG AND HEAVY TO FLY SMOOTHLY.

IT WON'T BE TOO HARD TO ESCAPE.

NUDGE, SCAT!

TUMBLE

BUMP

WATCH IT.

THANKS.

AH...

I CAN'T IMAGINE WHERE YOU CARRY THOSE.

I LOVE THE SOUND OF A BOMB DROPPING. ♥

......

EVERY-ONE OKAY?

I'M FINE.

LEG HURTS, BUT I'M OKAY.

ME TOO!

OKAY!

LET'S GET OUT OF HERE!

DRIP

DRIP

HAH...

I'M GUESSING A NEW PROTOTYPE.

SO...WHAT WAS WITH THE FLYING ERASERS?

BUT, MAN, THEY'RE FAILURES. THEY WERE HAVING A HARD TIME FLYING AND FIGHTING AT THE SAME TIME.

THEY WERE REALLY BAD FLIERS.

YEAH, THEY WERE LIKE A BUNCH OF IDIOTS TRYING TO DANCE.

FANG...

LOOK AT THE BLOOD...

CAN I DO SOMETHING?

HELP ME TAKE HIS SHIRT OFF. LET'S SEE WHAT WE'RE DEALING WITH HERE.

...THIS IS...

JUS' A SCRATCH.

YOU SHOULD HAVE TOLD US YOU WERE HURT!

STOP THE BLEEDING.

SHH!

DON'T TALK!

HOW?!

HOW WHAT?

PUT PRESSURE ON IT. PRESS A CLOTH OVER IT...

...AND LEAN ON THE WOUNDS WITH BOTH HANDS.

CLOTH...

NUDGE, RIP UP A SHIRT OR SOMETHING AND MAKE STRIPS FOR BANDAGES.

SSK

GUSH

GUSH

THERE'S TOO MUCH BLOOD... THIS ISN'T DOING MUCH.

MAX... SHOULDN'T WE TAKE HIM TO A HOSPITAL?

HOSPITAL... COULD BE DANGEROUS...

FANG COULD DIE!

HE'S LOSING TOO MUCH BLOOD...

THINK, MAX, THINK!

SHUDDER

SOMEONE'S COMING.

HUFF HUFF

TAP TAP

KIDS, YOU OKAY? WHAT ARE YOU DOING OUT HERE SO EARLY?

TMP

TMP

AH...

WHAT HAPPENED TO HIM?

WHAT DO I DO...?

I WANT TO GRAB EVERYONE AND RUN, BUT FANG'S HURT BAD...

OH MY...

UM, WE CAN TAKE CARE—

IS THIS 9-1-1?

YEAH, THERE'S A KID HERE—

SWOOSH

ARE YOU WITH HIM?

AH... YES.

WHAT'S HIS NAME?

HIS NAME IS... N-NICK.

NICK RIDE.

AND YOU ARE?

I'M MAX... M-A-X.

IS HE YOUR BOYFRIEND?

N-NO...

HE'S OUR BROTHER.

BROTHER?

PEEK

AH...WE... WE WERE ADOPTED. OUR PARENTS ARE... MISSIONARIES.

HMM... COULD YOU SIGN HERE?

AH... YES...

OH MY, DOCTOR!

......?

I THINK YOU NEED TO TAKE A LOOK AT THIS.

......!

TH-THIS IS...!!

AH...

YES, I AM.

ARE YOU NICK'S SISTER?

WHISPER

ARE YOU— LIKE HIM?

WHISPER

HOW DO YOU FEEL?

DIZZY AS A DODO BIRD.

KNOCK KNOCK

HUH? WHO IS IT?

CREAK

CAN WE TALK TO YOU FOR A MOMENT?

ERASERS?!

YOU MUST BE MAX, RIGHT?

NO... SOMETHING'S DIFFERENT.

WE'RE FROM THE FEDERAL BUREAU OF INVESTIGATION.

MY NAME IS ANNE WALKER.

FBI

AND WE'RE ON YOUR SIDE. WE JUST BECAME AWARE THAT YOU WERE HAVING SOME TROUBLE HERE...

...SO WE CAME TO SEE IF WE COULD HELP.

WHAT DO YOU WANT WITH US?

BEFORE THAT...

...YOU MUST BE HUNGRY. GO AHEAD AND EAT.

WAIT.

ANGEL, GIVE TOTAL SOME OF YOUR FOOD AND SEE IF HE KEELS OVER.

WHAT?!

SEE? IT'S OKAY TO EAT IT.

SSK

THERE'S NO NEED FOR THAT.

-GULP-

......

SO, HOW ARE YOU HERE TO HELP US? HOW DID YOU KNOW WE WERE HERE?

WE'LL ANSWER ALL YOUR QUESTIONS.

BUT...

...WE NEED YOU TO ANSWER SOME QUESTIONS TOO.

FINISH UP, AND THEN WE'LL TALK.

YAY! FOOD!

HMPH...

SO... WHAT'S YOUR NAME?

ARIEL.

OKAY, ARIEL. CAN YOU TELL ME WHAT YOUR RELATIONSHIP IS TO MAX?

SHE'S MY SISTER. YOU KNOW, BECAUSE OF THE MISSIONARIES. OUR PARENTS.

OKAY, I SEE. AND WHERE DID YOU GET YOUR DOG?

I FOUND HIM IN THE PARK.

SQUISH

HMM... OKAY.

FIDGET FIDGET

PEEK

IT'S ALMOST OVER, SWEETIE.

...OKAY...

ONE LAST QUESTION AND YOU CAN GO TO YOUR SISTER.

SSK

HAVE YOU
EVER HEARD
OF ANYONE
NAMED...

AND HOW DO YOU SPELL THAT?

CAPTAIN, LIKE THE CAPTAIN OF A SHIP.

AND THEN TERROR, YOU KNOW, T-E-R-O-R.

YOUR NAME IS CAPTAIN TERROR.

You missed an "R" there...

THAT'S RIGHT!

GRIN

ARE YOU REALLY FBI?

HA-HA-HA!

YES, I REALLY AM.

38

AND YOU WANTED TO KNOW MY AGE, RIGHT?

SMILE

SMILE

I'M EIGHT~!

EIGHT?!

STARTLE

YUP, EIGHT! HOW OLD ARE YOU?

UH... UM.

YOU'RE KIND OF TALL FOR AN EIGHT-YEAR-OLD, AREN'T YOU?

UH-HUH.

CREAK

WE'RE ALL TALL. AND SKINNY.

AND WE EAT A LOT. WHEN WE CAN GET IT.

GOSH, NO.

WHAT *IS* THAT?

YES, I SEE.

TELL ME... CAPTAIN, HAVE YOU EVER SEEN ANYTHING LIKE THIS?

......

AND YOU'RE BLIND?

UH-HUH.

RUB

WERE YOU BORN THAT WAY?

NO.

HOW DID YOU BECOME BLIND...

MOAN...

...UH, JEFF, IS IT?

YEAH, JEFF.

WELL, I LOOKED DIRECTLY AT THE SUN.

SIGH

YOU KNOW, THE WAY THEY ALWAYS TELL YOU NOT TO? IF ONLY I HAD LISTENED.

WHAT?

......

AND THEN I HAD, LIKE, THREE CHEESE-BURGERS.

BABBLE BABBLE

AND THEY WERE AWESOME, YOU KNOW? AND THOSE FRIED PIE THINGS?

THOSE APPLE PIES? MY BROTHER TOOK THEM, SO I DIDN'T GET TO EAT THEM. THEY LOOKED SO GOOD. HAVE YOU EVER TRIED THEM?

BABBLE

UH, I DON'T THINK SO.

CAN YOU SPELL YOUR NAME FOR ME?

UH-HUH. K-R-Y-S-T-A-L. I LIKE MY NAME. IT'S PRETTY. WHAT'S YOUR NAME?

SARAH. SARAH McCAULEY.

WELL, THAT'S AN OKAY NAME TOO. DO YOU WISH IT WAS SOMETHING DIFFERENT? LIKE, SOMETIMES I WISH MY NAME WAS KIND OF FANCIER, YOU KNOW? LIKE...CLEOPATRA. OR MARIE-SOPHIE-THERESE. DID YOU KNOW THAT THE QUEEN OF ENGLAND HAS, LIKE, SIX NAMES? HER NAME IS ELIZABETH ALEXANDRA MARY. HER LAST NAME IS WINDSOR. BUT SHE'S SO FAMOUS SHE JUST SIGNS HER NAME "ELIZABETH R," AND EVERYONE KNOWS WHO IT IS. I'D LIKE TO BE THAT FAMOUS SOMEDAY. I WOULD JUST SIGN "KRYSTAL."

BABBLE BABBLE BABBLE

UH...

......

YES?

?

HAVE YOU EVER HEARD OF A PLACE CALLED "THE SCHOOL"? WE THINK IT'S IN CALIFORNIA. HAVE YOU BEEN TO CALIFORNIA?

IT'S ALMOST SCARY TO ASK HER ANYTHING.

CALIFORNIA? LIKE, SURFERS AND MOVIE STARS AND EARTHQUAKES? NO. I'D LIKE TO GO. IS IT PRETTY?

HAVE YOU BEEN THERE, SARAH?

UH...I THINK THAT'S IT. YOU CAN GO NOW.

SMILE

HEE!

IS MAX SHORT FOR SOMETHING? MAXINE?

NO, IT'S JUST MAX.

I SEE. NOW, MAX, I THINK WE BOTH KNOW YOUR PARENTS AREN'T MISSIONARIES.

NO? WELL, FOR GOD'S SAKE, DON'T TELL THEM. THEY'D BE CRUSHED.

UM. TAKE A LOOK AT THIS.

THINKING THEY'RE DOING THE LORD'S WORK AND ALL.

THIS MAN IS JEB BATCHELDER.

DO YOU HAVE ANY KNOWLEDGE OF HIS WHEREABOUTS?

ANNE WALKER, WAS IT?

YES. HI AGAIN, MAX.

MAX, I'M NOT GONNA TELL YOU A BUNCH OF CRAP.

......

SO YOU SEE, WE CONSIDER YOU IMPORTANT. WE'D LIKE TO KNOW EVERYTHING ABOUT YOU.

...IF YOUR SO-CALLED FAMILY WERE TO FALL INTO THE WRONG HANDS.

BUT MORE IMPORTANT, IF THE STORIES ARE TRUE, THEN OUR ENTIRE COUNTRY'S SAFETY COULD BE AT STAKE...

YOU DON'T KNOW YOUR OWN POWER.

......

......

HMM...

HOW ABOUT WE MAKE A TRADE?

YOU GIVE US A CHANCE TO LEARN ABOUT YOU—IN NONPAINFUL, NONINVASIVE WAYS...

...AND WE'LL GIVE NICK THE BEST MEDICAL CARE AVAILABLE AND THE REST OF YOU A SAFE PLACE TO STAY.

AND I BELIEVE THAT THIS IS ALL STRAIGHT BECAUSE...?

IT WOULD BE GREAT IF I COULD OFFER YOU GUARANTEES, MAX. BUT I CAN'T—NOT ANYTHING THAT YOU WOULD BELIEVE.

I MEAN, COME ON. A WRITTEN CONTRACT? MY WORD OF HONOR? A REALLY SINCERE PROMISE FROM THE HEAD OF THE FBI?

BUT, MAX...

...YOU DON'T HAVE A LOT OF OPTIONS HERE.

......

WELL, SAY I ACCEPTED.

......

SMILE

WHERE'S THIS SAFE PLACE YOU'RE DANGLING IN FRONT OF ME?

MY HOUSE.

WHAT DO I DO...?

CREAK

MAX,
IS IT?

YES.
HOW DID
IT GO?

YOUR
BROTHER NICK—
IT WAS A LITTLE DICEY
FOR A WHILE. WE GAVE
HIM SEVERAL UNITS OF
BLOOD SUBSTITUTE, AND
IT BROUGHT HIS BLOOD
PRESSURE UP TO A
SAFE RANGE.

WE WERE
ABLE TO PATCH
UP HIS SIDE,
STOP ALL THE
HEMORRHAGING. A
MAIN ARTERY HAD
BEEN HIT, AND
ONE OF HIS...
AIR SACS.

SO
HOW IS HE
NOW?!

HE'S
HOLDING
STEADY.

PHEW...

FIDGET
FIDGET

IF NOTHING GOES WRONG, HE SHOULD BE OKAY. HE NEEDS TO TAKE IT EASY FOR MAYBE THREE WEEKS.

CAN I SEE HIM?

NOT TILL HE COMES OUT OF RECOVERY— MAYBE ANOTHER FORTY MINUTES.

AH...

THAT WOULD MEAN ABOUT SIX DAYS, GIVEN OUR FAST HEALING AND REGENERATIVE POWERS...

NOW, I'M HOPING YOU CAN FILL ME IN ON SOME PHYSIOLOGICAL STUFF...

...SINCE I NOTICED—

AH... UM...

THANK YOU, DOCTOR.

I'M SORRY, BUT THESE KIDS ARE TIRED AND NEED TO REST.

......

MAX!

HE'S GONNA BE FINE.

PHEW.

THAT'S GOOD TO HEAR!

...WELL, AS SOON AS F—NICK IS SOMEWHAT MOBILE...

AND...

...WE'LL GO TO ANNE'S HOUSE, REST UP, GET NICK UP TO A HUNDRED PERCENT. COOL?

NOD

SO FOR TONIGHT, WE'LL STAY HERE WITH FANG.

"FNICK"?

THIS IS HEAVEN COMPARED TO SLEEPING OUTSIDE.

WHEN DO I GET OUT OF HERE?

SIGH...

THEY SAY A WEEK.

SO, LIKE, TOMORROW?

THAT'S WHAT I'M THINKING.

PFFT!

HA...

SQUEEZE...

SIGH...

SHAAAA

PHEW...

RUB RUB

I CAN'T SHUT DOWN MY BRAIN... WAKING NIGHTMARES.

AND I FEEL SO HOT...WISH I COULD LIE DOWN IN SNOW.

SHUDDER!

GASP!

N-NO...

MY FACE FEELS THE SAME... AM I HALLUCINATING?

KNOW YOUR FRIENDS WELL; KNOW YOUR ENEMIES EVEN BETTER.

TAP

GASP!

WHAT...
WHAT WAS
THAT...?

THROB
THROB

SIGH...
THE VOICE
ALWAYS
SAYS STUFF
THAT GIVES
ME A HEAD-
ACHE...

I DON'T UNDER-STAND IT.

GUESS I'M GOOD TO GO.

NICK, UNTIL YOUR FULL RECOVERY, I'VE OFFERED FOR ALL OF YOU TO COME STAY AT MY HOUSE.

I ALREADY SPOKE WITH MAX, BUT WOULD THAT BE OKAY WITH YOU?

WHATEVER MAX SAYS.

SHE'S IN CHARGE.

HEH.

It's nice to hear such sweet words from you for a change.

I NEED TO GET OUT OF HERE.

THE HOSPITAL SMELLS ALONE ARE MAKING ME CRAWL THE WALLS.

OH, GOSH, IT'S SO PRETTY HERE.

WHAT'S YOUR HOUSE LIKE?

IS IT ALL WHITE WITH BIG COLUMNS? LIKE TARA? DID YOU SEE THAT MOVIE?

GONE WITH THE WIND?

NO, I'M AFRAID MY HOUSE ISN'T ANYTHING LIKE TARA.

IT'S AN OLD FARMHOUSE.

BUT I DO HAVE FIFTY ACRES OF LAND AROUND IT. PLENTY OF ROOM FOR YOU GUYS TO RUN AROUND.

WE'RE ALMOST THERE.

I HOPE YOU LIKE IT.

VROOM

SCREECH...

HERE WE ARE.

TAP

TAP

WOW...

THERE'S A POND OUT BACK. IT'S SHALLOW, SO IT MIGHT STILL BE WARM ENOUGH TO GO SWIMMING IN THE AFTERNOONS.

LET'S GO IN. I'LL SHOW YOU YOUR ROOMS.

PARADISE, HUH?

HEH-HEH.

MAXIMUM
RIDE

"CREAK"

PHEW...

MAX, THIS PLACE IS AWESOME!

THE BED'S SOFT, AND THE SHEETS SMELL SO NICE!

HA-HA. YEAH.

LET'S GO OUTSIDE!

I LOOKED OUT THE WINDOW, AND IT'S SO BEAUTIFUL, WITH THE POND AND ALL!

OKAY, LET'S ALL GO TOGETHER, GIVE IGGY SOME LAND-MARKS.

IT'S A BARN.

BARN?

LIKE, WITH ANIMALS?

WHAT IS THAT?

YEP, GUESS SO.

ARF!! ARF!

LET'S GO CHECK IT OUT!!

LISTEN, TOTAL.

NO MORE WITH THE BARKING. YOU'RE GOING TO SPOOK SOMEBODY.

WHINE...

CLACK...

LOOK!

COOL!

THAT FIRST ONE IS SUGAR.

NEEEGH..

HE'S BEAUTIFUL.

HE'S BIG.

BIG AND SWEET.

LOOK, THERE ARE MORE ANIMALS OVER THERE.

ANNE SEEMS TO LOVE ANIMALS. MAYBE SHE'S REALLY A GOOD PERSON.

MAYBE. I WONDER WHO'S FOR DINNER, THOUGH.

LOOK! THERE IS A POND!

TOLD YOU THE POND'S AWESOME!

WOW...

IT'S JUST SO BEAUTIFUL.

I'M GONNA SWIM!

WAI—

IT'S TIME FOR DINNER, CAPTAIN! WE CAN GO SWIMMING TOMORROW.

OKAY.

GOOD.

......

ARF!!

ARF!
ARF!!

TOTAL!
STOP
IT!

IT'S
HIS
YARD!

GLANCE

PUTZ.

AM I
HEARING
THINGS?

THIS IS IMPOSSIBLE! THESE NUMBERS AND CODES MAKE NO SENSE!

I'd rather take a math test!

I'M BEAT TOO.

IF THIS IS A COMPUTERIZED CODE, WE'LL NEVER BREAK IT.

KNOCK
KNOCK

YES?

CREAK

HEY, GUYS.

SLEEPY YET? KRYSTAL?

YEP, WE WERE JUST ABOUT TO CRASH.

GOOD. ANYONE NEED ANYTHING BEFORE YOU CRASH?

NO, WE'RE FINE.

ARIEL...

...HOW ABOUT LETTING TOTAL OUT ONE LAST TIME?

OKAY.

GOOD.

THEN SLEEP TIGHT, GUYS.

YOU TOO.

HMM...

GOOD MORNING, ANNE.

GOOD MORNING!

DID YOU MAKE YOUR BED?

NO, IT'LL JUST BE A MESS AGAIN AT NIGHT ANYWAY.

YOU SHOULD ALWAYS KEEP YOUR BED TIDY. IT'LL HELP YOU SLEEP BETTER.

OKAY.

HMM... SORRY.

I USUALLY HAVE A PROTEIN BAR FOR BREAK-FAST, SO...

IF IT'S OKAY, I'LL TRY.

You might get hurt.

JEFF IS A GOOD COOK!

YOU SURE? BUT YOU CAN'T SEE...

I'LL HELP.

I GUESS THAT'LL WORK.

IN THE MEANTIME, WE SHOULD DECIDE WHO'S DOING THE DISHES.

HUH?

WHAT IS THIS, CAMP AGENT?!

THE LOOK OF WONDER AND DELIGHT ON ANNE'S FACE MADE US FEEL LIKE MARVELS.

SO...

...AMAZING.

AND SHE REALLY DID TRY TO TAKE CARE OF US.

BUT AFTER THE FIRST DAY, I STARTED TO GET THE FLOCK READY FOR BED BEFORE SHE COULD DO IT.

IT BOTHERED ME, HER DOING IT. TAKING OVER MY ROLE.

SOON ANNE AND HER COMFY HOUSE WOULD BE JUST A MEMORY. JUST LIKE JEB. JUST LIKE DR. MARTINEZ AND ELLA.

HUM HUM

AND ALMOST TWO WEEKS PASSED BY...

KNOCK KNOCK

YEAH?

FANG.

CREAK

WHAT'S UP?

LOOK.

I WAS LOOKING AT THIS STUFF, GOING NUTS, YOU KNOW?

AND SUDDENLY IT LOOKED LIKE MAP COORDINATES.

THIS IS A BOOK OF DETAILED STREET MAPS OF WASHINGTON, D.C. I GOT IT OUT OF ANNE'S CAR.

LOOK— EACH PAGE IS NUMBERED, EACH MAP IS NUMBERED...

AND LOOK AT THIS CLUMP OF STUFF NEXT TO OUR NAMES...

BY GAZZY'S NAME, THERE'S 27, 8, G, 9.

...AND EACH GRID OF EACH MAP IS NUMBERED.

SO I GO TO PAGE 27, AND IT'S A SECTION OF TOWN, SEE?

YEAH.

THIS SECTION HAS TWELVE SMALLER MAPS. I GO TO MAP 8...

...WHICH IS A BLOWUP OF ONE SECTION.

THEN I GO TO COLUMN G AND TRACE IT DOWN TO ROW 9.

AND IT'S A PRETTY SPECIFIC LITTLE CHUNK OF STREETS.

OH MY GOD! YOU'RE SO BRILLIANT!

DID YOU TRY ANY OTHERS?

YEAH. THIS ONE BY NUDGE'S NAME. SAME THING— I ACTUALLY END UP WITH A REAL PLACE.

BUT I THOUGHT NUDGE WAS PRETTY SURE SHE'D FOUND HER PARENTS IN ARIZONA.

I DON'T KNOW. THE WOMAN WE SAW WAS BLACK, BUT IT WASN'T LIKE NUDGE WAS A PHOTOCOPY OF HER.

YOU THINK THIS IS WORTH CHECKING OUT?

ABSO-LUTELY.

EVERYONE ELSE ASLEEP?

YEAH. INCLUDING THE ANNA-MEISTER.

OKAY. GIMME A MINUTE TO GET SOME JEANS ON.

HMM.

NO PLACE WHERE SOMEONE COULD HAVE LIVED.

MAYBE THERE WAS AN APARTMENT BUILDING HERE, AND IT GOT TORN DOWN.

"BUILT IN 1954," SO I DON'T THINK SO.

OKAY. LET'S TRY THE NEXT ONE.

MAYBE WE'LL GET LUCKY THIS TIME.

AT LEAST IT'S A HOUSE.

LET'S CHECK IT OUT.

THERE'S NOTHING. THIS STINKS.

WHAT'S THIS?

YEAH. WELL, GET THIS LAST CLOSET AND WE'LL SPLIT.

NOTHING, I'M SURE.

THIS IS... GAZZY.

BABY GASMAN FOR SURE!

SHH!

DID YOU HEAR THAT?

HUH?

THEY'RE BACK!

VERY FUNNY. WELL, DON'T TAKE FOREVER. PRIMPING'S NOT GOING TO DO MUCH FOR YOU ANYWAY.

H-HOW IS THIS HAPPENING?

BUT WE'RE NOT SO DIFFERENT.

I'M PART OF YOU. YOU'RE PART OF ME.

EVERYTHING IS CONNECTED.

WE CAN HELP EACH OTHER.

NOD

YES.

...THANK YOU.

I'LL DO WHAT HAS TO BE DONE.

?

MAXIMUM
RIDE
CHAPTER 19

BOMBS
AWAY!!

SPIN.

SHOOOOOO

SPLASH!

AND DON'T HURT *ME!*

AH.

WATCH WHERE YOU DROP! YOU ALMOST LANDED ON ME!

SAY SORRY!

SORRY, SORRY!

......

SWISH

TAPPA

TAPPA
TAPPA

"FREEZE"

......

We are searching for a four-year-old girl, who disappeared at the park.

The disappearance of child

TEN KIDS HAVE GONE MISSING IN THE D.C. AREA OVER THE LAST FOUR MONTHS.

DID THE WHITECOATS TAKE THEM AS FODDER FOR THEIR EXPERIMENTS?

I CAN ONLY IMAGINE WHAT THE FAMILIES ARE GOING THROUGH.

WHAT HAPPENED WHEN WE WENT MISSING?

OUR PARENTS CARED, DIDN'T THEY? THEY MISSED US, RIGHT?

MAX!

YEAH, SWEETIE?

SPLASH

WHAT'S THE BEST WAY TO CATCH A FISH?

WELL...

...I GUESS IT DEPENDS ON THE KIND OF FISH.

NO, WHAT'S THE BEST WAY TO CATCH A FISH?

OH, I DON'T KNOW?

Look!

HAVE SOMEONE THROW IT TO YOU!

SWISH

HA-HA.

HA, GOOD ONE.

?!

Heh heh...

?

SSK

FWOSH

ANGEL?

YEAH?

ERM...

...CAN TOTAL, UM, TALK?

UH-HUH.

...HA HA.

DON'T TELL HIM I SAID THIS....

...BUT HE'S ACTUALLY NOT THAT INTERESTING.

TOTAL? ...CAN YOU TALK?

YEAH.

SO?

WHY DIDN'T YOU MENTION THIS BEFORE?

IT'S NOT LIKE I LIED ABOUT IT.

BETWEEN YOU AND ME...

...I'M STILL TRYING TO GET USED TO THE WHOLE FLYING-KID THING.

GRIN

HA-HA...

HAH...

KNOCK KNOCK

MAX? YOU AWAKE?

CREAK...

GAZZY? WHAT'S UP?

I CAN'T
SLEEP.

CAN
I GO FLY
AROUND?

HMMM.
OKAY.

LET'S
TAKE
ADVANTAGE
OF THE
WIDE-OPEN
SPACE.

MAX,
CAN I GO
TOO?

POP

PEEK

ME
TOO...

OKAY,
LET'S ALL
GO, THEN!
PUT YOUR
CLOTHES
ON.

THIS TOTALLY ROCKS!!

SPIN

MAX, LOOK! BATS!

THEY'RE MAMMALS, LIKE WE ARE.

MAMMALS? REALLY?

ARE THEY MORE LIKE US THAN BIRDS? WELL, NOT THE WHOLE EATING-INSECTS THING.

WOW—!

PHEW...

MAX, YOU HAVE WARP DRIVE!

A-AWE-SOME!

I WANT TO RIDE WITH YOU.

WHAT WAS THAT, MAX?

I THINK I JUST DEVELOPED A NEW SKILL.

SO...

...WE FOUND THAT PHOTO OF GAZZY AT THAT HOUSE. WHICH MEANS FANG'S MAP CODE MIGHT NOT BE A COMPLETE WASTE.

THERE ARE TWO MORE ADDRESSES TO CHECK OUT.

DO YOU GUYS WANT TO COME?

OF COURSE! DO YOU EVEN HAVE TO ASK?!

MY HEART'S POUNDING...

OKAY.

THIS IS REALLY EXCITING!

LET'S GO!

SO, ANGEL?

HUH?

HAVE YOU PICKED UP ANYTHING FROM ANNE, ABOUT ANYTHING? ANYTHING OFF?

NOT REALLY. FROM WHAT I CAN TELL, SHE DOES WORK FOR THE FBI. SHE DOES CARE ABOUT US...

...AND WANTS US TO BE HAPPY. SHE THINKS THE BOYS ARE SLOBS.

I'M BLIND. HOW AM I SUPPOSED TO MAKE EVERYTHING ALL TIDY?

YEAH, BECAUSE YOU'RE SO HANDICAPPED.

LIKE...

...YOU CAN'T BUILD BOMBS, OR COOK, OR WIN AT MONOPOLY.

......

PFFT...

YOU CAN'T TELL US ALL APART BY THE FEEL OF OUR SKIN OR FEATHERS.

ANYTHING ELSE?

HMM...

THERE IS SOMETHING SHE ISN'T TELLING US.

BUT I DON'T KNOW WHAT IT IS. IT'S NOT EVEN CLEAR IN HER MIND. JUST SOMETHING THAT'S GOING TO HAPPEN.

LIKE WHAT? IS SHE GOING TO TURN US OVER TO THE WHITECOATS?

I'M NOT SURE SHE EVEN KNOWS WHAT WHITECOATS ARE.

I DON'T KNOW THAT IT'S SOMETHING BAD.

IT COULD BE, LIKE—SHE'S GOING TO TAKE US TO THE CIRCUS OR SOMETHING.

WOULDN'T THAT BE REDUNDANT?

HMM. WELL...

...I KNOW HOW EASY IT'S BEEN TO RELAX THERE, GUYS.

BUT LET'S TRY TO KEEP ON GUARD, OKAY?

YO—FIRST ADDRESS IS DOWN THERE.

SHOWTIME.

MAYBE HER DAD WAS A BARBER?

YEAH, FANG, YOUR MOM WAS YOUNG SO...

SO ANOTHER BUST.

SWOON

I'M SORRY...

NO BIG. DIDN'T THINK IT WOULD ADD UP TO ANYTHING ANYWAY.

IT'S PROBABLY MORE WASTING OF OUR TIME, BUT SHOULD WE CHECK OUT THIS LAST ADDRESS?

YEAH, IT'S THE ONE NEXT TO IGGY'S NAME, RIGHT?

HE'S REALLY UPSET.

I KNOW, SWEETIE.

I DON'T CARE WHERE I CAME FROM.

WHEREVER I CAME FROM, I DON'T WANT TO GO BACK.

NOT IF YOU CAN'T COME TOO.

WE'LL DEAL WITH THAT IF AND WHEN IT HAPPENS.

BUT RIGHT NOW, LET'S CATCH UP TO EVERYONE ELSE.

ARE THERE APARTMENTS ABOVE THE STORES?

...NO.

WHAT'S ACROSS THE STREET?

A USED-CAR LOT.

I'M SORRY, IG.

IT'S MY FAULT, GUYS.

I THOUGHT I'D CRACKED THE CODE, BUT OBVIOUSLY I WAS TOTALLY OFF BASE.

WELL, IF YOU WERE WRONG, THEN WE DON'T HAVE TO BE DISAPPOINTED, RIGHT?

......

IT JUST MEANS WE STILL DON'T KNOW.

I'M SORRY, IG—

IGGY, YOUR HAND...

I DON'T CARE IF YOU'RE SORRY!!

EVERYONE'S SORRY!

THAT DOESN'T MATTER!

WHAT MATTERS IS THAT WE FIND WHERE WE BELONG!

I MEAN...

...I JUST CAN'T TAKE THIS ANYMORE!

I NEED SOME ANSWERS!

......

WE CAN'T JUST KEEP ON WANDERING FROM PLACE TO PLACE...

...ALWAYS ON THE RUN, ALWAYS HUNTED...

WE ALL WANT ANSWERS, IGGY...

WE ALL FEEL LOST SOMETIMES.

GRAB!

SSK... SSK...

IT'S JUST...

...WE HAVE TO STICK TOGETHER. WE WON'T STOP LOOKING FOR YOUR PARENTS, I SWEAR.

IT'S DIFFERENT FOR YOU.

YOU DON'T KNOW WHAT IT'S LIKE.

YEAH, I MAKE JOKES, I'M THE BLIND KID...

...BUT DON'T YOU SEE?

EVERY TIME WE MOVE ON, I'M LOST ALL OVER AGAIN.

YOU GUYS—IT'S SO MUCH EASIER FOR YOU. EVEN YOUR LOST ISN'T AS BAD AS MY LOST, YOU KNOW?

WE'RE YOUR EYES, IGGY.

YOU DON'T NEED TO SEE WHEN YOU'VE GOT US.

YEAH, BUT I WON'T ALWAYS HAVE YOU!

CLENCH...

WHAT HAPPENS IF YOU GET KILLED?

OF COURSE I NEED TO SEE, YOU IDIOT! I REMEMBER SEEING!

I KNOW WHAT IT'S LIKE! I DON'T HAVE IT ANY- MORE...

...AND I WON'T EVER HAVE IT AGAIN.

AND SOMEDAY I'M GOING TO LOSE YOU...

...LOSE ALL OF YOU...

...AND WHEN THAT HAPPENS...

...I'LL LOSE... MYSELF.

I DON'T CARE. LET THEM FIND ME, TAKE ME NOW.

IT DOESN'T MATTER. NOTHING MATTERS.

IGGY, LET'S GO!!

GET UP!

GIVE ME ONE GOOD REASON.

LISTEN, IGGY...I'M SORRY ABOUT TONIGHT. I KNOW HOW DISAPPOINTED YOU ARE.

WE'RE ALL DISAPPOINTED. AND I'M SORRY YOU'RE BLIND. I'M SORRY WE'RE MUTANT BIRD KIDS, I'M SORRY WE DON'T HAVE PARENTS...

...I'M SORRY WE HAVE ERASERS AND PEOPLE TRYING TO KILL US ALL THE TIME.

BUT IF YOU THINK I'M GOING TO LET YOU GIVE UP ON US NOW, YOU'VE GOT ANOTHER THING COMING. YES, YOU'RE A BLIND MUTANT FREAK...

...BUT YOU'RE MY BLIND MUTANT FREAK, AND YOU'RE COMING WITH ME—NOW!

WEEE!!!

OR I SWEAR...

...I'LL KICK YOUR SKINNY WHITE ASS FROM HERE TO THE MIDDLE OF NEXT WEEK.

IGGY, I NEED YOU. I LOVE YOU. I NEED ALL OF YOU...

...ALL FIVE OF YOU, TO FEEL WHOLE MYSELF.

NOW GET UP...

...BEFORE I KILL YOU!!

WELL, WHEN YOU PUT IT THAT WAY...

HERE, HOLD MY HAND...

RIIIIING

......

THANKS FOR MAKING DINNER, ANNE.

WHAT IS THIS? I MEAN— LOOKS GOOD.

AT LEAST I MADE A LOT OF IT. I'M LEARNING.

IT'S GREAT.

plaster

Don't overdo yourself.

IF YOU'RE ALL DONE WITH THE FOOD, I'D LIKE TO TALK TO YOU GUYS.

?

SORT OF A FAMILY MEETING.

YOU'VE ALL DONE BEAUTIFULLY HERE.

I THINK WE'RE READY TO TAKE THE NEXT STEP.

WHAAAT?!

WHOA, YOU HAD US GOING THERE FOR A MINUTE.

I'M NOT KIDDING, NICK.

THERE'S AN EXCELLENT SCHOOL NEARBY. IT WOULD BE PERFECTLY SAFE. YOU COULD MEET OTHER PEOPLE YOUR AGE, INTERACT WITH THEM.

AND—LET'S FACE IT: YOUR EDUCATION HAS BEEN SPOTTY AT BEST.

BOLT

YOU'LL START ON MONDAY. I'LL PICK UP YOUR UNIFORMS TOMORROW.

I LOOK LIKE PREP-SCHOOL BARBIE.

~YAWN~

ANGEL? NO FUNNY BUSINESS WITH THE TEACHERS, *COMPRENDE?*

GOTCHA.

CAN TOTAL COME?

NOPE.

OKAY, I'LL BRING THE CAR AROUND FRONT, SO HURRY AND GET READY.

GOOD MORNING, NICK.

GOOD MORNING, ANNE.

OH, AND JEFF.

YOU AND NICK WILL BE IN THE SAME CLASS. IT'LL HELP YOU GET YOUR BEARINGS.

......

OKAY.

WEAR JACKETS— IT'S CHILLY THIS MORNING.

I HOPE...WE ALL SURVIVE.

ZEPHYR, IS IT?

YEAH? THAT'S ME.

At least he's not Captain Terror anymore.

Yeah, Zephyr's a big improvement...

ZEPHYR, YOU'RE WITH ME.

ARIEL AND KRYSTAL? YOU GUYS COME WITH ME.

NICK? AND JEFF? I'M MRS. CHEATHAM. WELCOME TO OUR SCHOOL. COME WITH ME, AND I'LL SHOW YOU YOUR CLASSROOM.

OKAY.

THE TEACHERS SEEM OKAY. THEY DON'T REALLY LOOK LIKE POSSIBLE ERASERS.

BUT WE SHOULDN'T LET OUR GUARDS DOWN...I TRUST THEM TO KNOW WHAT TO DO.

OKAY.

MAX? I'M MS. SEGERDAHL. YOU'RE IN MY CLASS.

AND OUR SCHOOL DAY BEGAN.

NOW, DOES ANYONE REMEMBER THIS AREA'S NAME?

I DO.

YES, ARIEL?

IT'S THE YUCATÁN. PART OF MEXICO.

IT HAS CANCÚN, A POPULAR VACATION SPOT. AND MAYAN RUINS. AND IT'S CLOSE TO BELIZE. ITS PORTS ARE SOME OF THE CLOSEST TO AMERICA...

...SO IT'S CONVENIENT FOR DRUG RUNNERS TO SIPHON DRUGS UP FROM SOUTH AMERICA, THROUGH THE PORTS, AND THEN ON INTO TEXAS, LOUISIANA, AND FLORIDA.

VERY GOOD. DO YOU KNOW ANYTHING ABOUT THE YUCATÁN?

......

...AH...

...YES.

?

DO YOU KNOW WHERE THE DICTIONARY IS?

WHAT?

OUR REFERENCE MATERIALS ARE OVER THERE.

WHEN WE HAVE FREE STUDY TIME, YOU CAN WALK AROUND AND DO HOMEWORK.

AND THE COMPUTERS AND OTHER REFERENCES ARE OVER HERE.

OH. OKAY. THANKS.

NO PROBLEM.

WATCH THIS! I'M GONNA FLY!

YEAH?

LET'S SEE IT.

......

WAAH!

MY ARM!

WHAT WAS THAT?

TAKE HIM TO THE NURSE!

HEY YOU, NEWBIE!

WHAT'D YOU DO THAT FOR?

WHAT?

WHEN SOME WING NUT SAYS HE'S GONNA FLY, YOU TELL 'IM, "GET THE HECK DOWN FROM THERE!" YOU DON'T SAY, "LET'S SEE IT!" WHAT'S THE MATTER WITH YOU?

......

I DIDN'T KNOW.

WHAT, YOU GROW UP UNDER A ROCK?

I JUST DIDN'T KNOW.

YEAH, HE DIDN'T KNOW. 'CAUSE HE'S FROM THE PLANET DUMBASS.

WHERE DID YOU GET YOUR HAIR DONE?

WONDER HOW THE KIDS ARE DOING...

AH...

OVER HERE, HERE'S A COUPLE SPOTS.

OTHERWISE WE'LL HAVE TO SIT NEXT TO CHARI AND HER GANG.

DON'T MESS WITH THEM.

SO HOW'S SCHOOL?

OKAY, I GUESS.

WELL, LET ME KNOW IF YOU NEED ANY HELP!

MAXIMUM
RIDE
CHAPTER 21

CAPITAL OF PARAGUAY?

ASUNCIÓN. INHABITED PRINCIPALLY BY THE GUARANI.

ASUNCIÓN?

YES, THAT'S RIGHT, MAX. VERY GOOD.

GUESS THE VOICE CAN BE HANDY. FOR ONCE.

wow...

NOW LET'S TAKE OUT OUR SCIENCE WORKBOOKS.

HMM?

WHISPER WHISPER

KNOCK KNOCK

EXCUSE ME.

MAX?

THEY NEED YOU IN THE OFFICE FOR A MOMENT.

WHAT NOW? IS THIS IT? ARE THEY GOING TO TURN INTO ERASERS?

IN HERE.

HEY.

OH NO. THIS CAN'T BE GOOD.

ARE YOU MAXINE RIDE?

JUST MAX.

THESE ARE YOUR BROTHERS JEFF AND... ZEPHYR?

YES.

YOUR BROTHERS HAVE SET OFF...

...A STINK BOMB IN THE SECOND FLOOR BOYS' LAVATORY.

THAT'S IMPOSSIBLE.

THEY'RE NOT TROUBLE-MAKERS. THEY WOULDN'T DO ANYTHING LIKE THAT.

MY BROTHERS DON'T LIE!

THEY SAY THEY DIDN'T DO IT. THEY'RE LYING.

ALL CHILDREN LIE. CHILDREN ARE BORN KNOWING HOW TO LIE.

SMIRK

THEY'RE DIS-HONEST, DIS-RESPECTFUL, UNHOUSE-BROKEN ANIMALS. UNTIL WE GET TO THEM.

URK!

NOT MY BROTHERS.

OUR PARENTS ARE MISSIONARIES, DOING THE LORD'S WORK. WE WOULD NEVER LIE.

......

......

I KNOW YOUR BROTHERS ARE GUILTY. I KNOW YOU'RE PROTECTING THEM.

THIS IS THE LAST TIME YOU'LL GET AWAY WITH ANYTHING AT THIS SCHOOL.

PHEW...

WHAM...

YOU...!!

......

BUT THIS KID WAS A TOTAL JERK TO ME ON THE PLAY-GROUND.

AND SOMEONE STUCK A "KICK ME" SIGN ON THE BACK OF IGGY'S SHIRT.

SIGH...

GUYS, YOU'RE GOING TO MEET JERKS IN EVERY SITUATION.

FOR THE REST OF YOUR LIVES.

BUT YOU CAN'T BE DOING STUFF LIKE STINK BOMBS. WE'RE TRYING TO BLEND, REMEMBER?

SO THAT WAS NOT THE RIGHT WAY TO GO.

SORRY, MAX.

LISTEN, YOU TWO.

YOU PUT US ALL AT RISK.

FROM NOW ON YOU'RE GOING TO TOE THE LINE AT THIS STUPID SCHOOL OR YOU'RE GOING TO ANSWER TO ME. GOT IT?

...GOT IT.

YEAH, GOT IT. WE'LL BE MORE STUPID AND IDIOTIC IN THE FUTURE. WE'LL BLEND.

GOOD.

WE'RE HOME!

......

I GOT A PHONE CALL.

GLARE

I GUESS YOU'RE ALL ADJUSTING.

BUT LET ME JUST SAY THAT I'M VERY DISAPPOINTED IN YOUR BEHAVIOR.

WELL, ANYWAY, COME INTO THE KITCHEN.

THERE'S HOT CHOCOLATE AND COOKIES.

GRRR!

TSK.

HOT CHOCO-LATE AND COOKIES FOR YOU GUYS? ANNE'S TOO NICE.

THEY DESERVED THE STINK BOMB.

RUB RUB

BUT BE CAREFUL FROM NOW ON.

......

BE CAREFUL FROM NOW ON.

?

FWISH!!

GENTLY...

TAP!

WOW, ANGEL CAN JUMP HIGH!

Me too!

HOP

HOP

BECAUSE I'M A SWAN!

ANGEL...

WHEN MOST OF THE REGULAR PEOPLE ARE GONE...

AFTER MAX SAVES THE WORLD, MOST OF THE REGULAR PEOPLE WILL BE GONE.

BUT YOU AND THE OTHERS WILL HAVE A GREATER CHANCE OF SURVIVING.

YOU WERE DESIGNED TO SURVIVE.

...YOU WON'T HAVE TO HIDE YOUR WINGS ANYMORE.

HOP

YOU CAN HAVE IT.

I'M SAM.

YOU'RE IN MY LANGUAGE ARTS CLASS.

OH, OKAY. THANKS.

AH...

UM...

HE'S CUTE.

WHERE DID YOU MOVE FROM?

WOW. MIDWEST. THIS MUST BE PRETTY DIFFERENT FOR YOU.

SO, ARE YOU DOING SCHOOL-WORK OR MORE OF A PERSONAL PROJECT?

YEP.

UH...

MISSOURI.

UM...

WELL, HOLY MOLY.

TER BORCHT. HAVE I EVER HEARD THAT NAME BEFORE?

CLEARLY HE MUST HAVE BEEN INVOLVED WITH JEB, THE SCHOOL, THE WHITECOATS, AT SOME POINT.

I MEAN, HOW MANY INDEPENDENT EVIL GENETIC RESEARCHERS COULD THERE BE?

SURELY THEY ALL KEPT IN TOUCH, EXCHANGED NOTES...

...BUILT MUTANTS TOGETHER...

DASH!

THIS IS A HUGE BREAK-THROUGH.

I CAN'T WAIT TO TALK TO THE FLOCK ABOUT THIS.

HUH?

WE HAD GYM TODAY, AND EVERYONE LOOKED SO DUMB!

HA-HA.

OKAY. JUST CALM DOWN.

SO HE KISSED SOMEONE. BIG DEAL.

WHY SHOULD I EVEN CARE IF HE KISSES EVERY GIRL IN THE WHOLE SCHOOL?

HE'S LIKE MY...BROTHER.

He's not really my brother, but he's like one.

BLUSH!

MAYBE YOU HAVE FEELINGS FOR HIM.

NOOO.

SHUT UP, VOICE.

SHAKE

SHAKE

188

I WAS JUST SURPRISED.

NOW I'M OVER IT.

I'M FINE.

......

WHAT'S UP, MAX?

TRAINING TO BURN A HOLE IN MY HEAD JUST BY STARING AT IT?

GASP!!

NO, NO, NOTHING, NOTHING AT ALL!

THERE THEY ARE.

LITTLE BIRDS.

!!

SHUDDER!

SOMETHING'S COMING THIS WAY!

OH MY!

WHAT HAPPENED TO YOU?

ERASERS. I'M HUNGRY. IS THERE A SNACK?

WHAT ARE "ERASERS"?

WE'RE HUMAN-AVIAN HYBRIDS.

ERASERS ARE HUMAN-LUPINE HYBRIDS.

RABBITS?

THAT'S LAPIN. OR, MORE CORRECTLY, LEPORID. NOT LUPINE.

OH. WOLVES.

THEY ATTACKED YOU? WHERE DID THEY COME FROM? HOW DID THEY KNOW WHERE YOU WERE?

?

THEY ALWAYS ATTACK US. THEY'RE EVERYWHERE.

THEY WERE CREATED TO BE...WEAPONS, KIND OF. BACK AT THE SCHOOL, THEY WERE THE GUARDS, THE SECURITY, THE PUNISHERS.

SINCE WE ESCAPED, ERASERS HAVE BEEN TRACKING US.

ISN'T ALL THIS IN YOUR REPORTS?

I WAS WONDERING WHEN THEY'D SHOW UP.

THIS IS THE LONGEST WE'VE GONE WITHOUT THEM FINDING US.

WHY DIDN'T YOU TELL ME?

I REALLY THOUGHT YOU KNEW.

YOU KNEW A BUNCH OF OTHER STUFF ABOUT US.

I MEAN, I WASN'T KEEPING IT A SECRET OR ANYTHING.

WE'D HEARD ONLY VAGUE RUMORS.

THEY SEEMED SO FARFETCHED THAT WE DIDN'T BELIEVE THEM.

WELL, I'M GOING TO MAKE SOME PHONE CALLS.

NONE OF THE ERASERS HAVE LONG, STREAKED HAIR...

MAX!

AH, ANGEL...

WE HAVE A FIELD TRIP TOMORROW, MAX. YOU SHOULD GET SOME SLEEP.

YEAH, YOU'RE RIGHT...

ANGEL...

...DID YOU PICK UP ANYTHING FROM ARI?

DARK. RED. ANGRY. TORN. CONFUSED.

HE HATES US.

AND HE LOVES YOU.

HE LOVES YOU A LOT.

SSK...

WHAT?!

STARTLE!

THEY DOWN?

THEY'RE BEAT. SCHOOL REALLY TAKES IT OUT OF THEM.

AND THEN, OF COURSE, ERASERS.

YOU GUYS SHOULD GO TO BED TOO.

CLICK...

NUDGE IS ALREADY ASLEEP.

...HMPH.

LET THEM ENJOY IT WHILE THEY CAN.

SHE'S TAKING MY PLACE.

I CAN'T BE BOTH?

YOU THINK I'M A LOUSY MOM?

YOU'RE A FIGHTER, NOT A MOM.

WHAT, BECAUSE I'M NOT GIRLY ENOUGH, IS THAT IT?

TURN

NOT LIKE THAT GIRL WITH THE RED HAIR, STUCK TO YOU LIKE GLUE!

!

WHAT AM I SAYING?! I SOUND LIKE A JEALOUS IDIOT!

GASP

HMMM...

SSK

IT'S A SPECIAL TREAT!

NO CLASSES, NO HOME-WORK TODAY!

SO A FIELD TRIP IS BASICALLY JUST A TOUR?

AH, THAT'S ANGEL'S CLASS.

HELLO. YOU'RE ARIEL'S FRIENDS, RIGHT?

ARIEL WENT TO THE BATH-ROOM!

IT'S ARIEL'S BIG SISTER!

YOUR SISTER KNEW YOU'D BE WORRIED.

...TH-THANKS. SIR.

YOU'VE GOT YOURSELF A REMARK-ABLE LITTLE GIRL HERE.

ANGEL DIDN'T PLAY MIND-PUPPET WITH THE LEADER OF THE FREE WORLD, NOW, DID SHE?

OH MY, THANK YOU SO MUCH, SIR. IT'S AN HONOR...

AH— NO PROBLEM.

ZOOM IN.

To be continued in
MAXIMUM RIDE, Vol. 4!

BONUS PREVIEW:
DANIEL X: THE MANGA

Watch a whole new world come to life in the manga adaptation of **James Patterson's** #1 New York Times bestselling series with art by SeungHui Kye!

COMING FALL 2010!
DANIEL X

Yen Press

Daniel X © SueJack, Inc.
Illustrations © Hachette Book Group

JAMES PATTERSON'S

DANIEL X

Art by: SeungHui Kye

I WISH THAT I DIDN'T SOMETIMES, BUT...

...I REMEMBER EVERYTHING ABOUT THAT CURSED, UNSPEAKABLY UNHAPPY NIGHT TWELVE YEARS AGO...

DROP

THE LIST—

I KNOW WHAT IT IS:

THE LIST OF ALIEN OUTLAWS ON TERRA FIRMA.

AND I KNOW WHO I AM:

SON OF GRAFF, SON OF TERFDRON—

—THE ALIEN HUNTER.

NO LAST NAME.

JUST DANIEL X.

I HAVE TO TELL
YOU ONE LAST
THING ABOUT
THAT NIGHT.

I MUST GET
IT OUT.

EVEN THOUGH I WAS ONLY THREE
YEARS OLD, I AM ASHAMED THAT I DIDN'T
FIGHT THE PRAYER TO THE DEATH...

YOU'RE VERY IMPRESSIVE AND SCARY, ORKNG—

MAY I CALL YOU ORKNG?

GRRRRR

IS THAT YOUR LAST WISH?

OH, I HOPE NOT.

SAY, I'VE HEARD YOU HAVE LEVEL 4 STRENGTH.

TRUE OR FALSE?

WOW~!

THUD

AND YOU'RE A SHAPE-SHIFTER TOO?

YOU...

EXTERMI-
NATED.

TWELVE YEARS
HAVE PASSED
SINCE THAT NIGHT.

I'M
FIFTEEN
NOW.

ALL GROWN UP.
SORT OF.

SINCE MY
MOM AND DIED
DIED...

...SINCE I
BECAME
AN ALIEN
HUNTER...

...I'VE BEEN KIDNAPPED BY FACELESS METALLIC HUMANOIDS.

TWICE.

I'VE BEEN CHASED AND CAPTURED BY A SHAPE-SHIFTING PROTO-PLASM IN LONDON WHO WANTED TO MAKE ME INTO A JELLY SANDWICH WITHOUT THE BREAD.

I'VE BEEN IN HAND-TO-ANTENNAE COMBAT WITH AN ENTIRE CIVILIZATION OF INSECTS IN MEXICO CITY, CUERNAVACA, AND ACAPULCO.

I'VE HAD MY FACE RUN OVER AGAIN AND AGAIN FOR DAYS BY SELF-REPLICATING MACHINES THAT WERE ABOUT TO TAKE OVER DETROIT.

A BILLION OR SO "LITTLE WAILING MOUTHS" CONNECTED THROUGH AN ELECTRICAL NETWORK TO A SINGLE MIND ATE AND DIGESTED ME IN HAMBURG, GERMANY.

THEY WERE ALL ON THIS LIST, AND NOW THEY'RE ALL GONE.

LET ME CHECK.

THE LIST—

IT CONTAINS THE NAMES, FULL DESCRIPTIONS...

...AND APPROXIMATE WHEREABOUTS OF THE KNOWN OUTLAW ALIENS CURRENTLY ROAMING THE EARTH.

AND TRUST ME ON THIS—

THEY ARE OUT THERE, WATCHING AND STUDYING US.

NUMBER 6: ERGENT SETH.

HE'S BASED IN L.A., SOMEWHERE CALLED MALIBU.

HE SPECIALIZES IN GENOCIDE, AND HE'S ALREADY DEVASTATED ALPAR NOK.

NOW HE'S AFTER TERRA FIRMA—EARTH—TO DESTROY EVERY LIFE-FORM.

IT'S CRUCIAL TO STOP HIM BEFORE HE GETS ON A ROLL...

...SO THE LIST STRONGLY RECOMMENDS HIM AS THE NEXT TARGET.

DING DONG.

L.A....

TIME TO LEAVE THIS HOUSE.

HUH?

I NEVER HAVE VISITORS. WHO CAN IT BE?

GAH!

WHO SENT YOU AFTER ME?!

I WANT TO KNOW RIGHT NOW!!

HEHEHEHE HEH

URK!

SO—

NUMBER 6 SOMEHOW KNEW I WAS COMING.

WHAT OTHER POWERS DOES ERGENT SETH HAVE THAT ARE AS IMPRESSIVE AS MY OWN?

Keep reading in Volume 1!

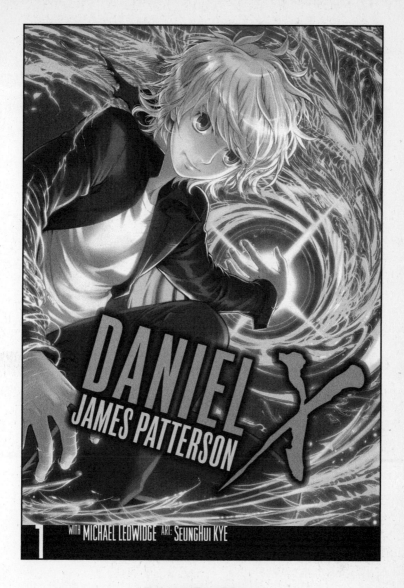

**Look for
DANIEL X: THE MANGA Vol. 1
in stores
October 2010!**

MAXIMUM RIDE: THE MANGA ③

JAMES PATTERSON
& NaRae Lee

Adaptation and Illustration: NaRae Lee

Lettering: Abigail Blackman

MAXIMUM RIDE, THE MANGA, Vol. 3 © 2010 by SueJack, Inc.

Illustrations © 2010 Hachette Book Group, Inc.

All rights reserved. Except as permitted under the U.S. Copyright Act of 1976, no part of this publication may be reproduced, distributed, or transmitted in any form or by any means, or stored in a database or retrieval system, without the prior written permission of the publisher.

The characters and events in this book are fictitious. Any similarity to real persons, living or dead, is coincidental and not intended by the author.

Yen Press
Hachette Book Group
237 Park Avenue, New York, NY 10017

www.HachetteBookGroup.com
www.YenPress.com

Yen Press is an imprint of Hachette Book Group, Inc. The Yen Press name and logo are trademarks of Hachette Book Group, Inc.

First Yen Press Edition: August 2010

ISBN: 978-0-7595-2969-4

10 9 8 7 6 5 4 3 2 1

BVG

Printed in the United States of America